ART DOSSIER junior

Original title: *Il taccuino segreto*
Text: Gloria Fossi
Translation: Catherine Frost
Illustrations: Gianluca Garofalo
Art director: Raffaele Anello

Photographs:
All illustrations belong to Archivio Giunti except Fotolia.com, p. 45 centre

www.giunti.it

© 2013 Giunti Editore S.p.A.
Via Bolognese 165 - 50139 Firenze - Italia
Via Borgogna 5 - 20122 Milano - Italia

First edition: June 2013

Reprint	Year
6 5 4 3 2 1 0	2016 2015 2014 2013

MISTO
Carta da fonti gestite
in maniera responsabile
FSC® C023532
FSC
www.fsc.org

Printed by Giunti Industrie Grafiche S.p.A. - Prato (Italy)

GLORIA FOSSI

The secret notebook

illustrations by
Gianluca Garofalo

A story with...

LEONARDO

G GIUNTI Junior

4

August 6, 1460

Dear Diary,
Today I'm writing you for the first time!
Yesterday was a very special day.
First of all because they told me that in Rome,
where the Pope lives, on August 5th
of many centuries ago, a kind of miracle happened:
it snowed in August. Like magic!
And then because… even if it's not snowing here
but is really hot instead and the cicadas
are singing like they always do in summer,
something wonderful has happened to me,
so strange it almost doesn't seem true.

But first of all, Diary, let me introduce myself.
My name is Leonardo.
I'm eight years old and I live in Vinci, a little town
in the hills surrounded by woods and streams and vineyards.
Now I'm sitting under the olive trees
with their silvery leaves blowing in the wind.
I can hear the bells ringing loud and clear, even from the nearby
villages, on the other hills and down in the valley.

I made you all by myself, to record the thoughts that pass
through my head. I always have so many projects in mind,
I had to find a place to keep them! So I took some big sheets
down from the shelf where my grandfather keeps
the parchment paper he uses to do the accounts. I cut them
into pages with a thin blade and I fastened them all together.

I've decided that I will always keep you in my jacket pocket,
so I can write in the fields, sitting astride
the lowest branch of the big oak tree
or on a rock at the top of a hill, wherever I want!
I'll tie your covers together with a little leather string
and keep you in my pocket as safe as a treasure.

And, dear Diary, I want to fill you with drawings.
Everything around me is so interesting!
Dad and Granddad are always laughing at me
because my head is "bursting with ideas",
but they don't even see those strange animals,
funny houses and even towns that sometimes
seem to leap out of spots on walls. And clouds too.
They never realise that clouds always look like something,
maybe a horse and rider or a man puffing out his cheeks.

9

But now I have to tell you about
what happened to me yesterday. Well, I've just come back
from Florence, where my Dad is a notary. Yesterday he came
to get me. He pulled me up on his horse Rocco and we set off
at a gallop, down through the valley. You can't imagine how beautiful
Rocco is! He is strong, slender and fast, and he has such long legs!

10

As we were riding, I told Dad how I wanted to draw his horse:
rearing up, standing at rest, or carrying a rider on his back.
Dad didn't say anything, he just looked at me
with a strange smile on his lips.
Suddenly we saw the beautiful city of Florence.
What a sight it is when you come down out
of the hills and see that dome so high
it seems to touch the clouds!

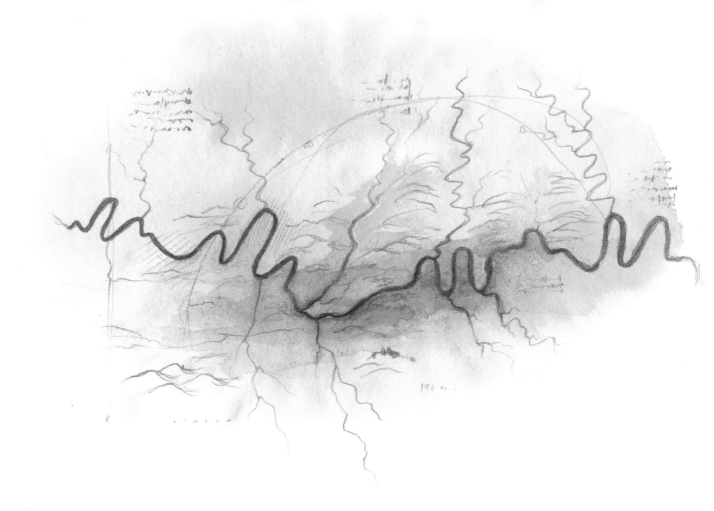

We rode down the hillside and along the banks
of the River Arno. Dad told me that the river starts way up
in the mountains, far away, beyond the great dome,
and flows past Florence, through the valley below Vinci
and then down to the sea, near Pisa.

I suddenly got a great idea.
I will draw a map of the Arno seen from above,
just like the birds see it!
When I told Dad he answered me with a laugh,
"You always have some outlandish idea
rolling around in your head!"

By then we had entered the city.
In Florence there are hundreds of shops
where the craftsmen work silver and gold, like magicians.
The biggest and best workshop, I think,
is the one of a great artist called
Andrea del Verrocchio.
In his shop they make everything:
bronze and silver armour, wooden picture frames,
stone and marble busts of famous men and ladies,
so beautiful they seem alive.

Verrocchio also paints pictures on big wooden panels
for merchants' houses, or for churches. When I grow up
I want to paint beautiful ladies and pictures for churches too,
and not just on wood or linen, but also on walls.
I want to be an artist like Verrocchio,
because he can do just anything!

We were walking through Florence when Dad said to me:
"You know, Leonardo, I was hoping you would be a notary like me when you grew up. You would have signed important contracts and everybody would have looked up to you. Except that…"
"Except what?"
"A few days ago I showed some of your drawings to Verrocchio in his workshop, and then I saw that you were going to follow a different profession."
"What?"
"It's time to stop daydreaming now, you're almost grown up! You are going to work in his shop, starting next autumn. There will be lots of boys like you there to learn the trade."

"Stop daydreaming?"

After news like this?

I'm going to learn the trade, I'm going to become an artist!

It's the most exciting news in the world, isn't it?

And since this will be the last summer I spend at Vinci,

I want to record all my ideas on your pages,

and all the interesting things I see.

And then, dear Diary, I will keep you forever.

august 9

Hello, Diary!
I'm a big boy now and they let me run around alone
in the fields, where nature shows me all her secrets
and gives me thousands of new ideas.

For example: I like to watch the changing seasons.
In spring I see the flowers blooming in the grass
around the olive trees. In May I can pick sweet cherries.
Then I love to climb on the branches of the great oak
and look under the leaves for the acorns.

What a strange shape they have!

I wonder why pigs like them so much.

Today I have decided to keep everything I write
a secret between you and me, Diary. It will be easy to do,
because I'm left-handed and it comes natural to me
to write backwards! When I begin a sentence, my hand starts off
from right to left. I dare anybody to read my writing!

And then I'm sort of messy because I have too many ideas.
That's why I make a drawing, then turn the sheet
over and jot down a thought that has popped
into my mind. Then I start doing something else.
Then I come back and do another drawing.
I have a top-secret code!

Dear Diary, here I am again!
Today I built a little cart with wheels, to play with.
First I made a drawing of it, after carefully
observing the carts the farmers use.
Then I took some pieces of wood that I found
in a corner of the hayloft. The cart was finished
in no time. But the cart the farmers use
is big, and they have a mule to pull it.
Mine runs downhill instead,
at breakneck speed!

I would like to make a cart that moves by itself,
without anybody pushing it. I would call it
a 'mechanical wagon'. Or an 'automated machine'.
I could even make one all shielded, to be used in war,
that "most bestial madness", as Uncle Francesco calls it.
And then if soldiers should come here with canons,
we could get inside it and fight them off.
Uncle Francesco told me you can build things like that,
because he has seen them himself.

He told me about a strange man who came to town
one day when he was a child playing in the market square.
The man was a kind of magician with a long white beard
and a turban on his head, like one of the Three Wise Men.
He came from a distant land, on the other side
of the mountains, beyond the great stretch of sea,
where the land is made of sand as fine as dust
and instead of horses they use strange animals
with humps on their backs.

The magician sat down on a bench and began
to talk about enchanted cities, where scientists study
the stars, mathematics and geometry, and know
how to make wonderful things.

For example, Uncle Francesco remembers a clock
that worked by water power, and another one
shaped like an elephant that lifted its foot
and waved its trunk around! And then there was
a knight almost as big as I am, dressed in shining armour,
who walked a few steps and raised his arm.
But the most frightening toy was a devil that threw open his arms
and stuck out his fiery tongue.
My uncle told me that these strange toys
were called "automatons".

I want to build an "automaton" too.
I want to invent a little drum that plays by itself
and makes a lot of noise.
When my grandfather Antonio is making fun of me,
he says I'm too crazy about these "bizarre inventions".

august 18

Dear Diary,

It's true, Dad and Granddad Antonio

are always telling me to stop daydreaming.

Because I'm always looking far away,

beyond the window, toward the clouds.

And even above the clouds, where the birds fly high and free.

They say I'm not like the other children in the village.

They get their fun by chasing hens and piglets

down the narrow streets.

But for me, it's no fun to scare animals.
The animals should be free, like we are.

I remember once my father took me to Florence
to see the lions. We came to a little street
behind Piazza della Signoria, where there was
a big rectangular cage called a "menagerie".
Inside it were real lions, in flesh and blood!
And nearby was a market where they sold live birds.
Suddenly I realised that I can't stand to see animals
locked up in cages.
"Please", I begged Dad, "let's free the birds at least,
so they can fly away!"

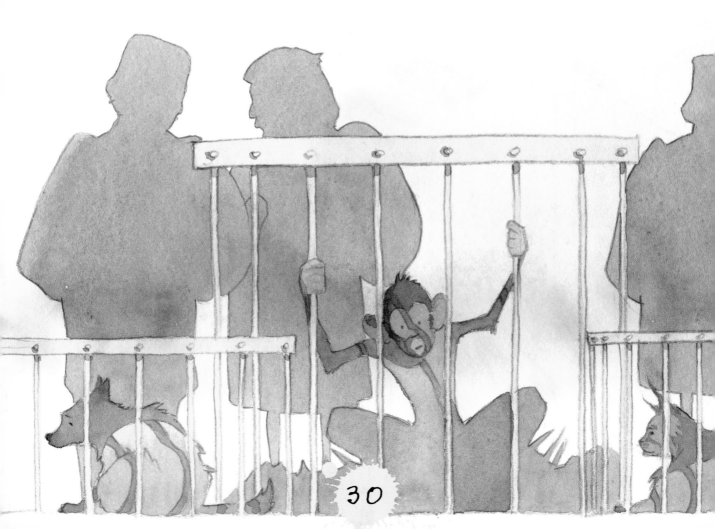

But he didn't even answer me, just laughed.
I really think this instead. I want to start working soon,
so I can buy those birds, open all the cages
and set them free to fly away at last.

Could anything be more wonderful
than flying from one branch to another, the way birds do?
Like the swallows that will come back tonight to the castle tower
as the sun is setting, in the light of the summer evening?
Flight is something magic. I wonder what birds see from up there.
And how happy they must be. You can tell from the way they sing!
I wish I could fly too … so I could draw a picture
of this great valley stretching far away,
down to the sea.

Dear Diary, this is something I can't wait to tell you.
A few days ago, walking in the woods,
I arrived at the door of a cave, so dark
that even I (who am usually so brave!) was afraid.
I was too scared to go inside, so I only took a quick look.

And guess what I saw?
Nothing at all!!!
But… and now comes the good part!
Inside, in the dark, I began to imagine that a great dragon
was hiding, his mouth wide open, his tongue as red
as the devil my uncle told me about, with the body
of a wolf and the tail of a snake.
I imagined him so clearly that I frightened myself
and had to run away fast!

Then the other day, I saw a farmer cutting a round panel
out of an old tree trunk. It was so beautiful,
it reminded me of the things Verrocchio makes.
So I asked him for it. Then I took my brushes and colours
to paint it, and suddenly I remembered the cave.

I drew the monster on it and copied from life
those little snakes you see in the fields,
the ones that scare you to death but are really harmless.
I painted his skin green like a lizard.
Then I hid and waited for Dad to come home,
leaving only one little candle lit.
He almost fainted
from the fright!!!
I still can't stop
laughing…

Dear Diary, I haven't written for days now!
Yesterday Dad came to take me to Florence on Rocco.
From a distance I heard the clattering of his hooves
and I ran out to meet them.
Something must have frightened
the horse, because he suddenly
reared. But I managed
to stop him, by grabbing
the bridle and holding on fast!

When I grow up, I want
to model a horse in clay,
and if I'm able, I'll put a knight
in armour on his back.

Uncle Francesco told me that the ancient sculptors poured red-hot liquid bronze into a terracotta model to make a great monument that would last throughout the seasons.

He saw one like that in Rome, where there are
ancient monuments everywhere.
Maybe when I'm grown I can go there
to see them for myself!

Dear Diary,

Today I'm sitting under the olive tree for the last time,
in the shade, drawing a picture.
Thanks to you, I've had hundreds of new ideas!
I've decided that one day I'll invent a flying machine,
made out of a cage and bat's wings.
And then I'll build a wooden lion. His chest will open up
and lilies will drop out of it.
Tomorrow I'm leaving for Florence,
where I will finally start to work in Verrocchio's shop.
I will become an artist, I'll invent new machines,
I'll discover many things.

And I'll always keep a notebook like this,
where I can write down and illustrate every idea
that springs into my mind.
Now I'm going to close you for the last time,
tie a good knot in your little string and hide you
under a board in the ceiling.
When I come back to get you, I'll be an old man.
You will be the guardian of my dreams,
and I will never forget you!

It's all true!

Did you think this story was invented? It's all true instead!

Here are the characters in the story. You can imagine it like a film, even though it all happened over five hundred years ago!

• Leonardo's father, **Ser Piero da Vinci**, was a notary who worked in Florence.

• His grandfather Antonio and his uncle Francesco lived in Vinci, a town about forty kilometres from Florence.

• Leonardo was born on **April 15, 1452**. He spent the first years of his life with his grandfather and his uncle. Then he went to Florence to study art in Verrocchio's workshop.

He was a handsome boy, with thick curly hair framing his face. He loved freedom for himself and for others. He was strong enough to bend a horseshoe with his hands. His master Verrocchio may have used his face as model for his bronze statue of the young **David**. He always observed nature, animals and the mysteries of the universe. He knew how to look, and was never distracted. And he left us everything written in his notebooks, which he made himself. He wrote and drew in these notebooks, carrying the smaller ones around with him wherever he went.

Vinci

Among the thousands of drawings he left us are many studies of horses, cats, falcons, snakes, swallows and other birds. As well as imaginary monsters. Over five hundred years have passed; and yet his writings are still full of mystery. Many secrets about the things he wrote and drew have not yet been revealed.